What's My Style?

I love creating elaborate patterns packed with detail so I can do lots of intricate coloring. I try to use as many colors as possible. Then, I layer on lots of fun details. Here are some more examples of my work.

With my love of detail and coloring, I can easily fill up entire pages of journals like these!

Tips and Techniques

WHERE TO START

You might find putting color on a fresh page stressful. It's ok! Here are a few tricks I use to get the ink flowing.

Do you like warm colors?

How about cool colors?

Maybe you like warm and cool colors together!

Start with an easy decision. If a design has leaves, without a doubt, that's where I start. No matter how wacky and colorful everything else gets, I always color the leaves in my illustrations green. I have no reason for it, it's just how it is! Try to find something in the design to help ground you by making an easy color decision: leaves are green, the sky is blue, etc.

Get inspired. Take a good look at everything in the illustration. You chose to color it for a reason. One little piece that you love will jump out and say, "Color me! Use red, please!" Or maybe it will say blue, or pink, or green. Just relax—it will let you know.

Follow your instincts. What colors do you love? Are you a big fan of purple? Or maybe yellow is your favorite. If you love it, use it!

Just go for it. Close your eyes, pick up a color, point to a spot on the illustration, and start! Sometimes starting is the hardest part, but it's the fastest way to finish!

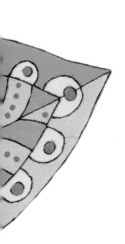

HELPFUL HINTS

There is no right or wrong. All colors work together, so don't be scared to mix it up. The results can be surprising!

Try it. Test your chosen colors on scrap paper before you start coloring your design. You can also test blending techniques and how to use different shapes and patterns for detail work—you can see how different media will blend with or show up on top of your chosen colors. I even use the paper to clean my markers or pens if necessary.

Make a color chart. A color chart is like a test paper for every single color you have! It provides a more accurate way to choose colors than selecting them based on the color of the marker's cap. To make a color chart, color a swatch with each marker, colored pencil, gel pen, etc. Label each swatch with the name or number of the marker so you can easily find it later.

Keep going. Even if you think you've ruined a piece, work through it. I go through the same cycle with my coloring: I love a piece at the beginning, and by the halfway point I nearly always dislike it. Sometimes by the end I love it again, and sometimes I don't, and that's ok. It's important to remember that you're coloring for you—no one else. If you really don't like a piece at the end, stash it away and remember that you learned something. You know what not to do next time. My studio drawers are full of everything from duds to masterpieces!

Be patient. Let markers, gel pens, and paints dry thoroughly between each layer. There's nothing worse than smudging a cluster of freshly inked dots across the page with your hand. Just give them a minute to dry and you can move on to the next layer.

Use caution. Juicy/inky markers can "spit" when you uncap them. Open them away from your art piece.

Work from light to dark. It's much easier to make something darker gradually than to lighten it.

Shade with gray. A mid-tone lavender-gray marker is perfect for adding shadows to your artwork, giving it depth and making it pop right off the page!

Try blending fluid. If you like working with alcohol-based markers, a refillable bottle of blending fluid or a blending pen is a great investment. Aside from enabling you to easily blend colors together, it can help clean up unwanted splatters or mistakes—it may not take some colors away completely, but it will certainly lighten them. I use it to clean the body of my markers as I'm constantly smudging them with inky fingers. When a marker is running out of ink, I find adding a few drops of blending fluid to the ink barrel will make it last a bit longer.

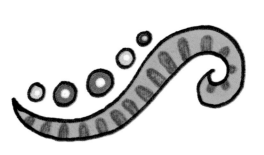

LAYERING AND BLENDING

I love layering and blending colors. It's a great way to create shading and give your finished piece lots of depth and dimension. The trick is to work from the lightest color to the darkest and then go over everything again with the lightest shade to keep the color smooth and bring all the layers together.

1 Apply a base layer with the lightest color.

2 Add the middle color, using it to create shading.

3 Smooth out the color by going over everything with the lightest color.

4 Add the darkest color, giving your shading even more depth. Use the middle color to go over the same area you colored in Step 2.

5 Go over everything with the lightest color as you did in Step 3.

PATTERNING AND DETAILS

Layering and blending will give your coloring depth and dimension. Adding patterning and details will really bring it to life. If you're not convinced, try adding a few details to one of your colored pieces with a white gel pen—that baby will make magic happen! Have fun adding all of the dots, doodles, and swirls you can imagine.

1 Once you've finished your coloring, blending, and layering, go back and add simple patterning like lines or dots. You can add your patterns in black or color. For this leaf, I used two different shades of green pen.

2 Now it's time to add some fun details using paint pens or gel pens. Here, I used white, yellow, and more green.

This design really pops with lots of patterning and little details.

Coloring Supplies

I'm always asked about the mediums I use to color my illustrations. The answer would be really long if I listed every single thing, so here are a few of my favorites. Keep in mind, these are *my* favorites. When you color, you should use YOUR favorites!

Alcohol-based markers. I have many, and a variety of brands. My favorites have a brush nib—it's so versatile. A brush nib is perfect for tiny, tight corners, but also able to cover a large, open space easily. I find I rarely get streaking, and if I do, it's usually because the ink is running low!

Fine-tip pens. Just like with markers, I have lots of different pens. I use them for my layers of detail work and for the itsy bitsy spots my markers can't get into.

Paint pens. These are wonderful! Because the ink is usually opaque, they stand out really well against a dark base color. I use extra fine point pens for their precision. Some paint pens are water based, so I can use a brush to blend the colors and create a cool watercolor effect.

Gel pens. I have a few, but I usually stick to white and neon colors that will stand out on top of dark base colors or other mediums.

Hello Angel #1121, Color by Hello Angel

Hello Angel #1099, Color by Hello Angel

Hello Angel #1097, Color by Ninna Hellman

Hello Angel #1114, Color by Hello Angel

Hello Angel #1126, Color by Dawn Collins

Hello Angel #1104, Color by Hello Angel

Hello Angel #1107, Color by Hello Angel

Hello Angel #1112, Color by Dawn Collins

Hello Angel #1101, Color by Dawn Collins

Hello Angel #1101, Color by Elaine Sampson

Hello Angel #1120, Color by Elaine Sampson

Hello Angel #1112, Color by Elaine Sampson

Hello Angel #1126, Color by Darla Tjelmeland

Turn off your mind, relax,
and float downstream.

—THE BEATLES, *TOMORROW NEVER KNOWS*

_____
_____
_____
_____
_____
_____
_____
_____

The life and love we create is
the life and love we live.

—UNKNOWN

_____
_____
_____
_____
_____
_____
_____
_____
_____
_____

The inspiration you seek is already within you.
Be silent and listen.

—RUMI

If you obey all the rules, you miss all the fun.

—KATHARINE HEPBURN

_____
_____
_____
_____
_____
_____
_____
_____

Your mind will answer most questions if you learn to relax and wait for the answer.

—William S. Burroughs

How beautiful it is to do nothing,
and then to rest afterward.

—SPANISH PROVERB

To love someone is nothing, to be loved by someone is something, but to be loved by the one you love is everything.

—UNKNOWN

Whatever comes, let it come. Whatever stays,
let it stay. Whatever goes, let it go.

—Unknown

Relax and be free.
You don't have to prove anything.

—UNKNOWN

_____
_____
_____
_____
_____
_____
_____
_____
_____

There's never enough time to do
all the nothing you want.

—BILL WATTERSON, *CALVIN & HOBBES*

Now and then, it's good to pause in our pursuit of happiness and just be happy.

—GUILLAUME APOLLINAIRE

The best and most beautiful things in the
world cannot be seen or even touched;
they must be felt with the heart.

—HELEN KELLER

Sometimes it's okay if the only thing
you did today was breathe.

—Unknown

Take it all one day at a time and
enjoy the journey.

—UNKNOWN

_____
_____
_____
_____
_____
_____
_____
_____
_____

Never be afraid to sit awhile and think.

—LORRAINE HANSBERRY

Let go a little and just let life happen.

—UNKNOWN

Where there is love there is life.

—Mahatma Gandhi

Don't underestimate the value of Doing Nothing, of just going along, listening to all the things you can't hear, and not bothering.

—WINNIE-THE-POOH

Throw KINDNESS around like CONFETTI

The most important thing is to enjoy your life—to be happy—it's all that matters.

—AUDREY HEPBURN

The time to relax is when you
don't have time for it.

—UNKNOWN

Almost everything will work again if
you unplug it for a few minutes...
including you.

—Anne Lamott

Don't look for love. Love will find you.

—UNKNOWN

_____
_____
_____
_____
_____
_____
_____
_____
_____
_____

At some point, you gotta let go, and sit still, and allow contentment to come to you.

—ELIZABETH GILBERT, *EAT, PRAY, LOVE*

You are my happy place.

—UNKNOWN

Love is when you sit beside someone doing nothing, yet you feel perfectly happy.

—UNKNOWN

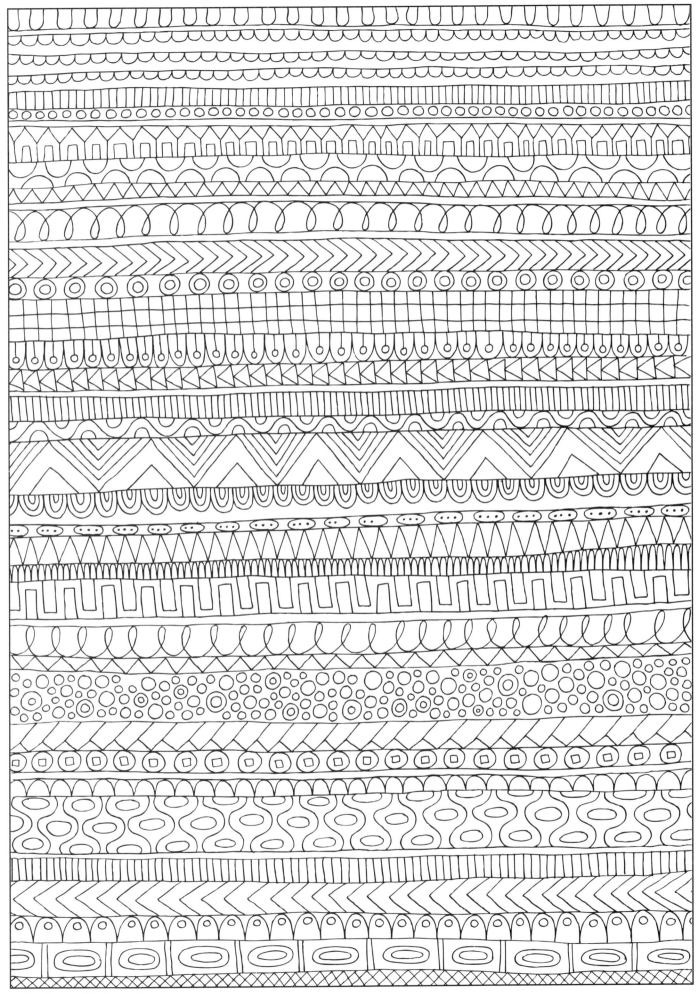

Time you enjoy wasting was not wasted.

—JOHN LENNON

Where we love is home, home that our feet
may leave, but not our hearts.

—OLIVER WENDELL HOLMES, *HOMESICK IN HEAVEN*

_____

_____

_____

_____

_____

_____

_____

_____

_____

_____

Breathe in peace. Breathe out love.

—UNKNOWN

I'm much more me when I'm with you.

—UNKNOWN

_____
_____
_____
_____
_____
_____
_____
_____
_____
_____

Hello Angel #1125

Put it all away, sit quietly, and just breathe.

—Unknown

Slow down. Rushing means you
miss what's right here.

—Unknown

You don't always need a plan.
Sometimes you just need to breathe,
trust, let go, and see what happens.

—MANDY HALE